Abraham Lincoln

Abraham Lincoln

Academic Industries, Inc.
West Haven, Connecticut 06516

ISBN 0-88301-782-2

Published by
Academic Industries, Inc.
The Academic Building
Saw Mill Road
West Haven, Connecticut 06516

Printed in the United States of America

Abraham Lincoln

Contents

President Abraham Lincoln held the United States together through the Civil War. It was he who signed the order freeing the slaves, making the war a fight for equal rights for all.

The Farm Boy

Abe did grow. In a few years, he was planting corn . . .

plowing fields . . .

and chopping wood.

Sometimes he and his sister went to school.

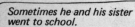

We're lucky there's a school. Many people never learn to read and write.

You're smart, Abe! You're learning quickly.

The only book the Lincolns owned was a Bible. Abe read every word.

In 1816 . . . There are too many slave-owners moving into Kentucky. It's no place for a poor man. We'll go to Indiana.

The new state of Indiana did not allow people to own slaves.

So the Lincolns packed their things and moved.

Pigeon Creek is the name of the settlement. It's not big, but it will grow.

Their first new home was only a lean-to.

What's that noise?

Only wolves. They won't bother us.

In the next few years Abe worked harder than ever, helping to clear land for crops and build a cabin.

Things will soon be easier.

But the next year, many people in the settlement became sick.

They call it the milk-sick. Some of our neighbors have died of it!

Abe's mother became sick, too.

I feel weak and hot. I don't know what's the matter!

Not long afterward, Nancy Lincoln died.

Sally tried to take her mother's place.

I don't know how to make candles. I can't make soap either, so everything is dirty.

Oh, Abe!

You're only a little girl! The worst thing is just missing our mother!

One day Tom Lincoln rode away.

Did Pa say where he was going?

Not a word!

Pa's been gone for days! Do you think anything bad could have happened?

I don't know. Riding through the woods alone is dangerous.

17

Suddenly, they heard noises outside.

Abe! Sally! I've been to Kentucky to get married. Come and meet your new mama.

Sarah Bush Lincoln was good and kind. Quickly she took charge of her new family.

We need a big fire and lots of hot water. Throw out those dirty bearskins. I have clean featherbeds and quilts.

Soon, both house and children were changed.

How do you like having two new sisters?

Just fine!

The two families were happy together. Sarah loved all the children.

But Abe was her favorite.

I'm glad you like to read, son. I wish I knew how.

Oh, yes! I want to know so much— and everything I want to know is in books!

But there were not many books around.

My best friend is a man who can give me a book I haven't read!

Abe would walk miles to borrow a book.

Thank you, Mr. Pitcher! I'll take good care of it!

I'm glad to help anyone who will walk thirty miles to read a book!

And he would get up early or stay up late to have time to read it.

A boy your age shouldn't be wasting time on such a foolish thing.

19

One day, Sarah learned that a school would open nearby.

I want the children to go to school.

The younger ones, maybe . . . but not Abe! He can make money splitting fence rails.

But he wants to go to school more than any of the other children!

I'm sorry. We need the money he can earn.

Until a boy was twenty-one, his wages belonged to his father.

So Abe spent most of his time working. All in all, he never went to school for more than a year.

But he would walk fifteen miles to the county courthouse.

What are you doing here, Abe?

I learn by listening to the lawyers present their cases.

And most nights he went to the country store.

The Louisville paper came today, Abe. The fellows are waiting to hear you read the news to them.

There's nothing I'd like better!

20

Traveler
and Soldier

When Abe was nine-teen . . .

Allen Gentry is taking a flatboat to New Orleans, and his pa has hired me to help him!

He'll pay me $8.00 a month, and I'll have a chance to see the country!

And a big city, too!

The trip down the river was an adventure. Sometimes there were storms.

They saw many steamboats.

It's like a floating palace!

Look at it go!

23

Let's go! I can't watch this!

People shouldn't be sold like animals!

It's not against the law here. Slaves are just property.

It's not right for one man to own another!

The trip down the river had taken a month. After the goods and flatboat were sold, they went home in a week by steamboat.

There's Rockport, Abe! We're almost home!

It was good of your pa to let me make this trip. I'll never forget it!

Abe worked for his father for two more years. Then one day his father had news for him.

Son, we're moving to Illinois. You can do what you like, now that you're twenty-one.

I'll come, too—long enough to help you get settled.

25

They traveled by ox-cart. After they arrived, Abe helped build fences and a new cabin.

Then he told his family that he was leaving.

Ma, I've got a job in a store in New Salem.

I'll miss you, Abe. But it's right for you to go.

In his new job and his new town, Abe soon made friends.

He charged me six cents too much, and he walked six miles to return the money. I call him "Honest Abe."

When I've no men around, Abe Lincoln carries water from the river for me.

Abe Lincoln's not only the smartest man in the county—he's the fastest and the strongest!

Abe joined the New Salem Debating Society.

That was a fine talk, Abe!

I thought he would give us a funny talk. But he has more than fun in his head!

Abe, you should go to work in the government.

We'll vote for you!

Why not give it a try?

Abe thought they had a good idea. But in March, 1832, a war broke out with the Blackhawk Indians. So Abe and other New Salem men joined the militia.

We need a captain. I vote for Abe Lincoln.

Abe it is! We all want Abe Lincoln.

Thank you, men. Nothing will ever please me more than being chosen your captain!

27

When the war was over, it was only two weeks before the election. Abe lost.

You got quite a few votes, Abe.

But not enough people knew about you.

Before the next election in 1834, Abe had time to talk to people and to make speeches.

We need better roads and public schools. Every child should have a chance to go to school!

That year he won the election.

He also studied law.

In 1837, when he was twenty-eight years old, he got a lawyer's license.

He left New Salem for Springfield, the state capital, to work in a law office.

Welcome, Abe! We'll change that sign to say *Stuart and Lincoln!*

Congressman
and
President

Soon he had many new friends. One night he went to a dance.

Mr. Lincoln, I want you to meet my sister, Mary Todd. She's from Kentucky.

Miss Todd, I want to dance with you in the worst way!

Abe was not a very good dancer.

Ouch!

Excuse me! I'm sorry!

The dance ended.

Mr. Lincoln, you got your wish. You danced with me in the *worst* way!

But Mary Todd did not really care how Abe danced. She was pretty and popular, but it was Abe she fell in love with. She believed in him.

She wrote to a friend.

I said once I would marry a man who would be president of the United States. I have met the man. He is Abe Lincoln.

We must stop it—even if it means paying the slave-owners for their slaves.

This country cannot be half-slave and half-free!

At the end of his term, Abe decided not to run again.

It's time I went back to being a lawyer.

I'm sad. The country needs men like you!

At home again, Lincoln soon became known as one of the best lawyers in Illinois.

But in 1854, Abe became interested in the government again.

Senator Douglas has asked for a new law that would allow slaves in parts of the country where they are now forbidden! That is wrong!

Lincoln began to make speeches against slavery.

My faith teaches me that all men are equal, no matter what their color.

He was asked to run for senator against Stephen Douglas.

I'll run! And I'll debate the question of slavery with Douglas.

Douglas agreed to the debates. Many people came to hear the two men speak.

The long and the short of it!

The Little Giant—and Abe, the Giant-Killer!

Douglas won the elction for senator. But the great debates made Lincoln known all over the United States.

In 1860, he was nominated for president.

Douglas will be running against me.

This time you'll win! *You* will be president!

He received letters from old and new friends.

A little girl from New York State says that I would look better if I grew a beard. It would make more women vote for me!

Maybe she's right!

And soon Abe started growing a beard.

He traveled around the country giving speeches, but on election night, November 6, he was in Springfield.

You've won! Congratulations, Mr. President!

I must tell Mary the news!

The people of Springfield shouted for joy.

But the southern states were not pleased by the election.

South Carolina no longer wants to belong to the United States of America.

By February, seven states had withdrawn from the United States to form a new government.

On March 4, 1861, Lincoln took office as president. In his speech, he spoke again and again to the people of the South.

I have no plan to stop slavery in the states where it is already accepted. I have no right to do so.

In *your* hands, fellow countrymen, and not in mine, lies the question of civil war!

Lincoln
and
the Civil War

But on April 12, Confederate soldiers attacked Fort Sumter. The Civil War had begun.

From morning until night there were always crowds of people at Lincoln's office door.

Sir, you can't see all of them!

I must try. Everyone has a right to talk to his president.

He met with his generals.

Mr. President, we have no army!

I have called for 75,000 soldiers from state militias.

He also spoke with his cabinet.

Sir, the newspapers and the people are crying for our side to win!

I cannot seem to find a general who will fight and win battles!

39

He still found time to keep a promise.

Here's the pony I promised you for coming to Washington and leaving your friends!

For a long time, the war went badly for the Union. Then, in 1862, things began to change. Lincoln spoke to his cabinet.

I want to free all slaves in the southern states. You told me to wait till we won a battle. Now we've done that!

Lincoln signed the order on January 1, 1863. It was read aloud by army officers in the South.

You hear that?

Forever free!

God bless Father Abraham!

Lincoln was elected again in 1864. At his inauguration he made another speech.

Let us bind up the nation's wounds.

On April 9, the southern army surrendered.

The fighting is over. The killing is ended! I'm glad I lived to see it.

A few nights later, Lincoln went to the theater.

A man named John Wilkes Booth crept to the door of the president's box.

He raised a gun and fired. Then he jumped to the stage.

Stop him! He has shot the president!

The next day Lincoln died.

41

POCKET BIOGRAPHIES

A train carried Lincoln's body home to Illinois. All across the country, people wept as it passed.

Lincoln was dead, but no one would forget what he stood for.

THE END

The Lincoln Memorial in Washington has become a gathering place for those who work to prove that all men are created equal.

Do you remember?

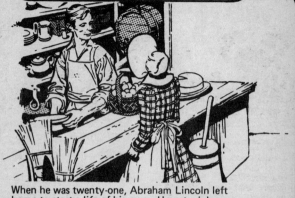

When he was twenty-one, Abraham Lincoln left home to start a life of his own. He got a job as a:

a. rail-splitter.   b. storekeeper.   c. lawyer.

People liked and trusted Abe Lincoln. He decided to go into politics but also studied:

a. law.   b. medicine.   c. teaching.

Lincoln was elected to Congress. He went to Washington. There it made him sad to see:

a. slave markets.   b. pollution.
          c. strict and unfair laws.

When Confederate soldiers fired on Fort Sumter, a war began. Lincoln was president during this war. It was:

a. the Spanish-American War.   b. the Civil War.
          c. World War I.

Quiz
Yourself

(Answers at end of section)

Words to know

waterfront	the place where ships dock
forbidden	• not allowed
nominated	chosen by one's party to run for public office
inauguration	a ceremony for a person elected to high office
surrendered	gave up

Can you use them?

Using the words above, complete the following sentences.

1. In 1976, the Republicans _____ Gerald Ford for president of the United States.

2. When Japan _____ in 1945, World War II ended.

3. Going without shoes in public buildings is _____ .

4. At his _____ , the new governor spoke to the people who had come to see him take office.

5. Many shops and restaurants lined the _____ where visitors to the islands first arrived.

Using pictures

In reading illustrated stories, you will find it helpful to "read" the pictures as well as the words. Look at this picture. It shows Abe Lincoln playing with his children. Abe's wife always said that Abe's heart was as big as his arms were long. Now turn to page 27 to find another example of Abe's love for his children.

Now turn to page 27 to find another example of Abe's love for his children.

While you are reading

Abraham Lincoln was a thoughtful person. Even as a boy he thought of other people before himself. What things did Lincoln do during his lifetime to show his concern for other people? While you are reading, list your answers below.

_____

_____

_____

_____

_____

_____

How well did you read?

When you have finished reading, answer the following questions.

1. Why wouldn't Abe's father let him go to school?

   (Check the correct *answers.*)

   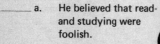

   _____ a. He believed that read- and studying were foolish.

   _____ b. He was afraid that the other children would laugh at Abe because he was so tall.

   _____ c. He needed the money Abe could earn splitting fence rails.

   _____ d. He thought that Abe wasn't smart enough to learn anything.

2. What things did young Abe Lincoln see during his trip to New Orleans on the flatboat?

   (Check the correct *answers.*)

   _____ a. beautiful homes

   _____ b. steamboats

   _____ c. many parks

   _____ d. great churches

   _____ e. a large market

   _____ f. a slave auction

3. Who did Abe always say was his best friend?

    (Check the correct answer.)

    _____ a.   a lawyer who argued
                 cases at the county
                 courthouse

    _____ b.   a man who could
                 give him a book
                 he hadn't read

    _____ c.   a senator named
                 Stephen Douglas

    _____ d.   his wife, Mary

    _____ e.   an actor named
                 John Wilkes Booth

4. Why did Abe Lincoln grow a beard?

    (Check the correct answer.)

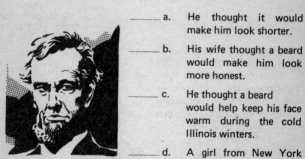

    _____ a.   He thought it would
                 make him look shorter.

    _____ b.   His wife thought a beard
                 would make him look
                 more honest.

    _____ c.   He thought a beard
                 would help keep his face
                 warm during the cold
                 Illinois winters.

    _____ d.   A girl from New York
                 said that more women
                 would vote for him if he
                 had a beard.

5. By what nicknames was Lincoln known?

(Check the correct *answers.*)

_____ a. "the Yankee President"

_____ b. "the New Salem Rail Splitter"

_____ c. "the Giant Killer"

_____ d. "the Slave President"

_____ e. "Honest Abe"

Using what you've read

People used many words to describe Abe Lincoln. They said that he was smart, strong, fast, and kind. A word used to describe a person, place, or thing is called an *adjective*. Make a list of some adjectives that you think describe yourself. Be sure to think of both your good qualities and the things about yourself that you might want to change.

ANSWER KEY

ABRAHAM LINCOLN

Can you use them?

1. nominated
2. surrendered
3. forbidden
4. inauguration
5. waterfront

How well did you read?

1. a, c
2. a, b, d, f
3. b
4. d
5. c, e

NOTES

NOTES

NOTES

NOTES

COMPLETE LIST OF POCKET CLASSICS AVAILABLE

CLASSICS

COMPLETE LIST OF POCKET CLASSICS AVAILABLE
(cont'd)

COMPLETE LIST OF POCKET CLASSICS AVAILABLE
(cont'd)

SHAKESPEARE

BIOGRAPHIES

B 1 Charles Lindbergh
B 2 Amelia Earhart
B 3 Houdini
B 4 Walt Disney
B 5 Davy Crockett
B 6 Daniel Boone
B 7 Elvis Presley
B 8 The Beatles
B 9 Benjamin Franklin
B10 Martin Luther King, Jr.
B11 Abraham Lincoln
B12 Franklin D. Roosevelt
B13 George Washington
B14 Thomas Jefferson
B15 Madame Curie
B16 Albert Einstein
B17 Thomas Edison
B18 Alexander Graham Bell
B19 Vince Lombardi
B20 Pelé
B21 Babe Ruth
B22 Jackie Robinson
B23 Jim Thorpe
B24 Althea Gibson